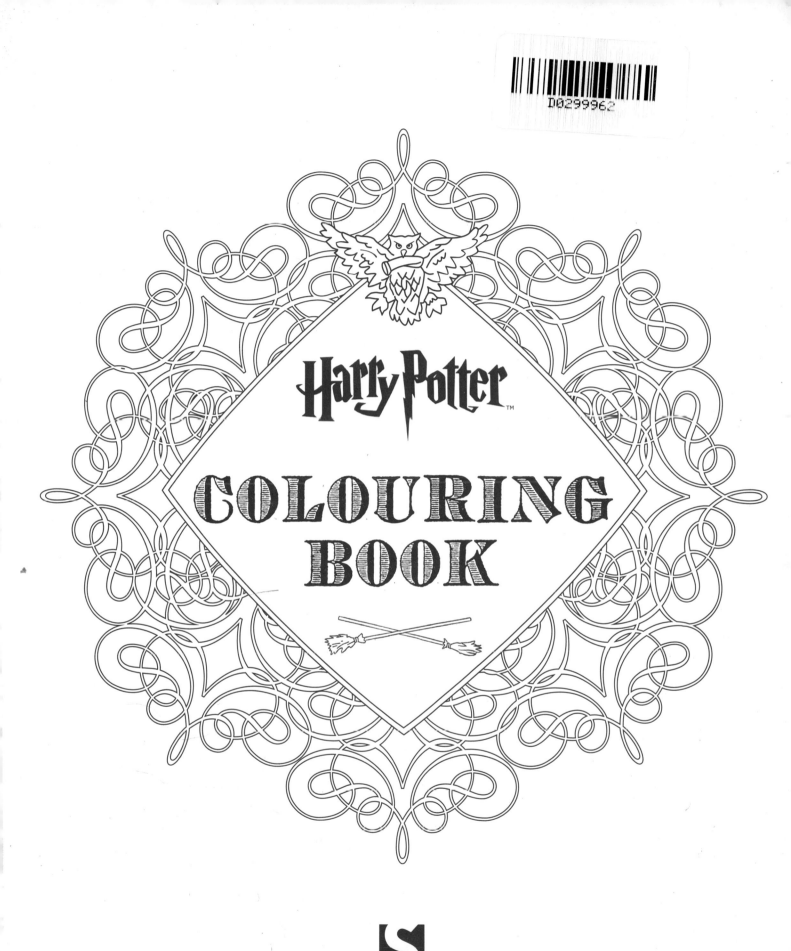

Harry Potter™

COLOURING BOOK

STUDIO PRESS

An Insight Editions Book

From the orange, brown, and green hues used to convey the warmth and whimsy of the Weasley family to the emerald green and silver of Slytherin house, colour was an essential element in bringing Harry Potter to life on-screen and achieving an atmosphere full of enchantment.

Let the film stills, unit photography, and concept art provided at the end of this book serve as both guide and inspiration as you explore the colour of the Harry Potter films.

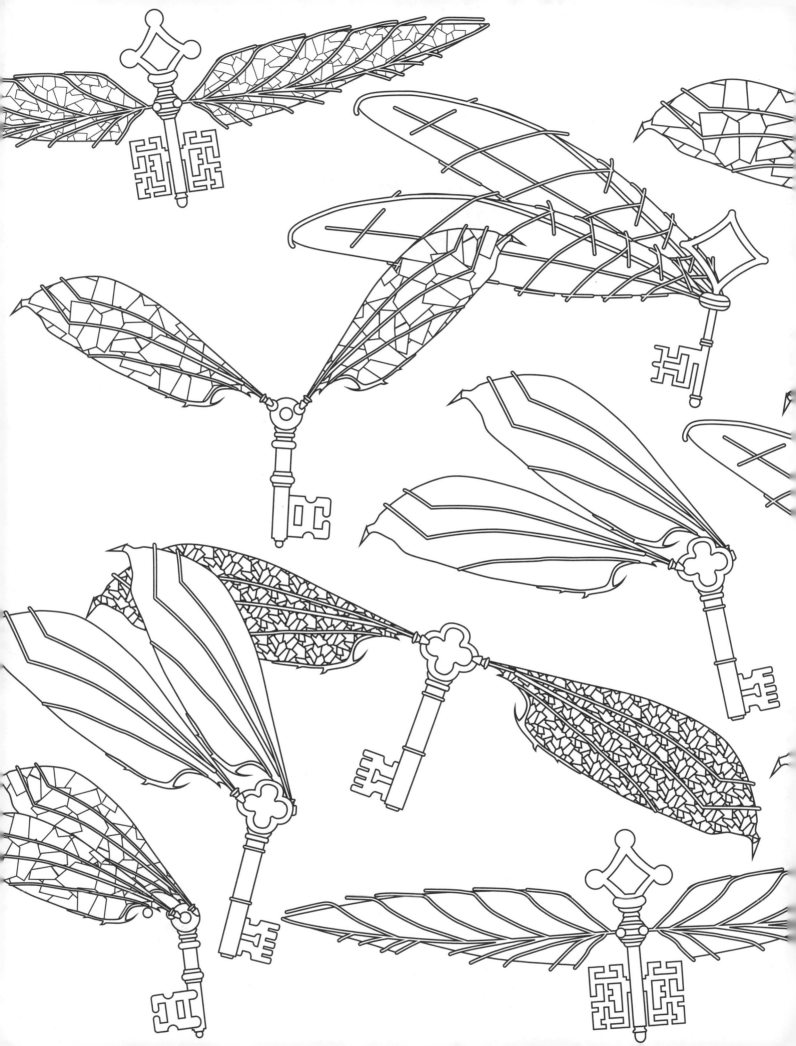

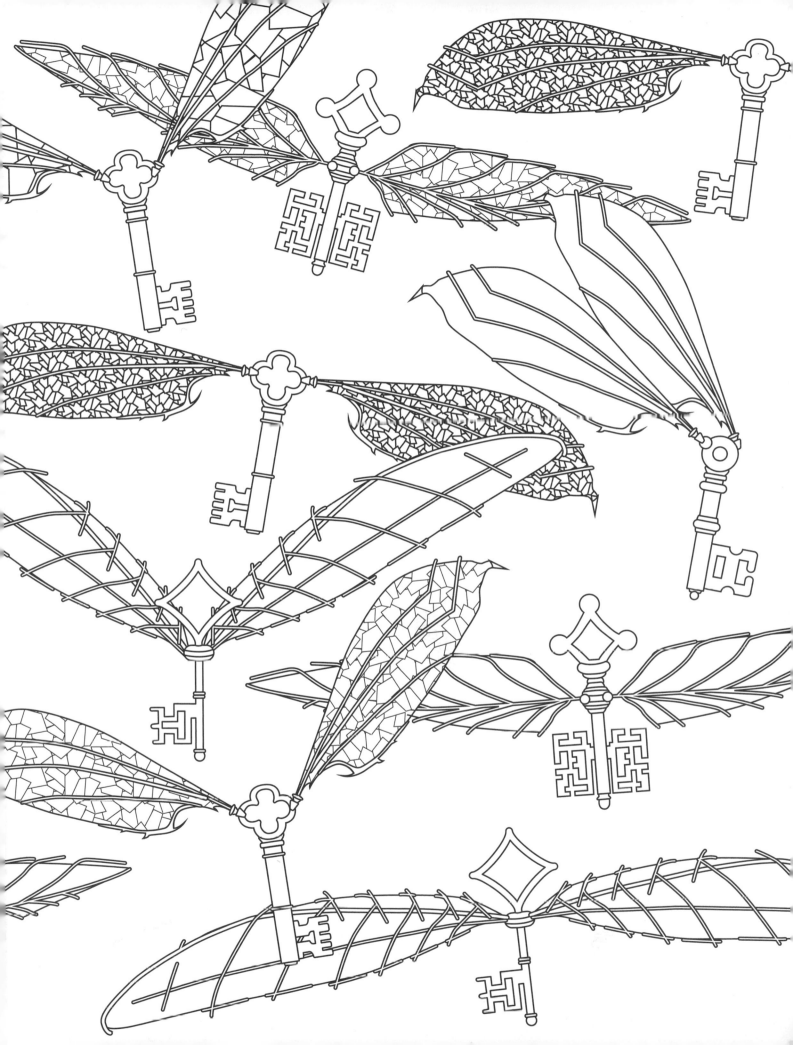

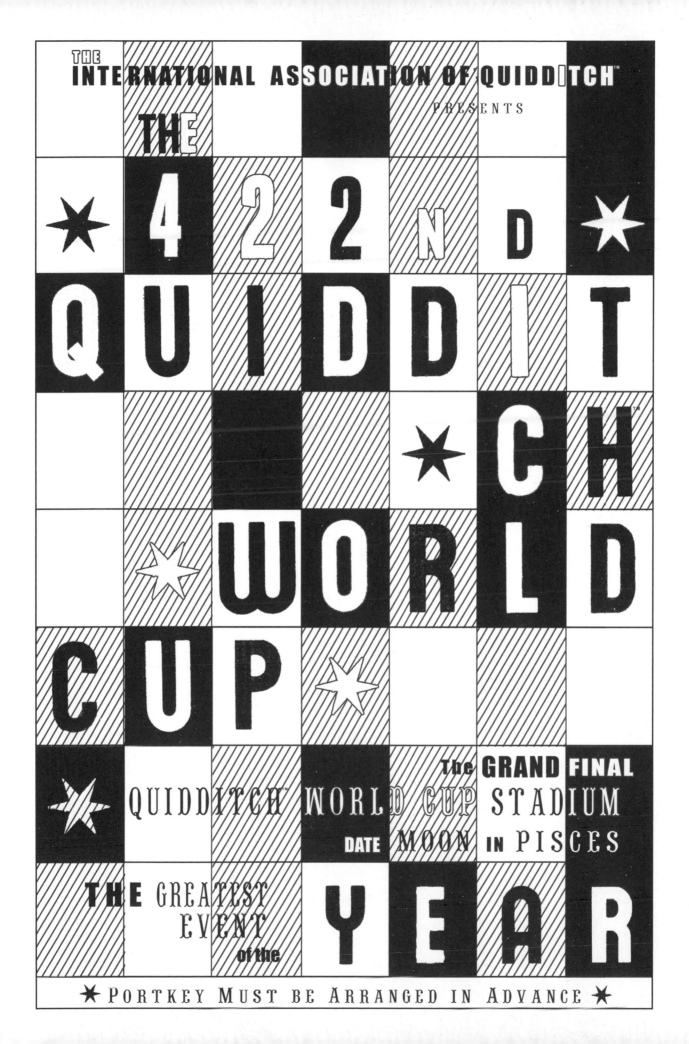

SLYTHERIN™

KEEP OFF THE DIRIGIBLE PLUMS

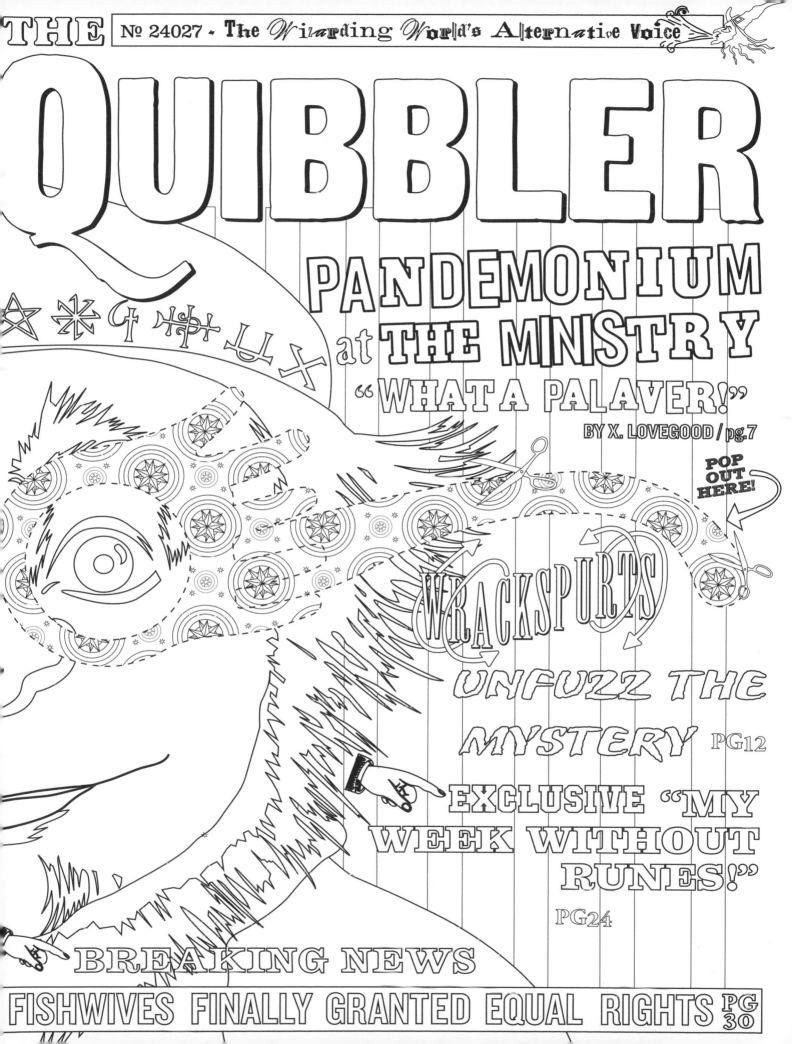

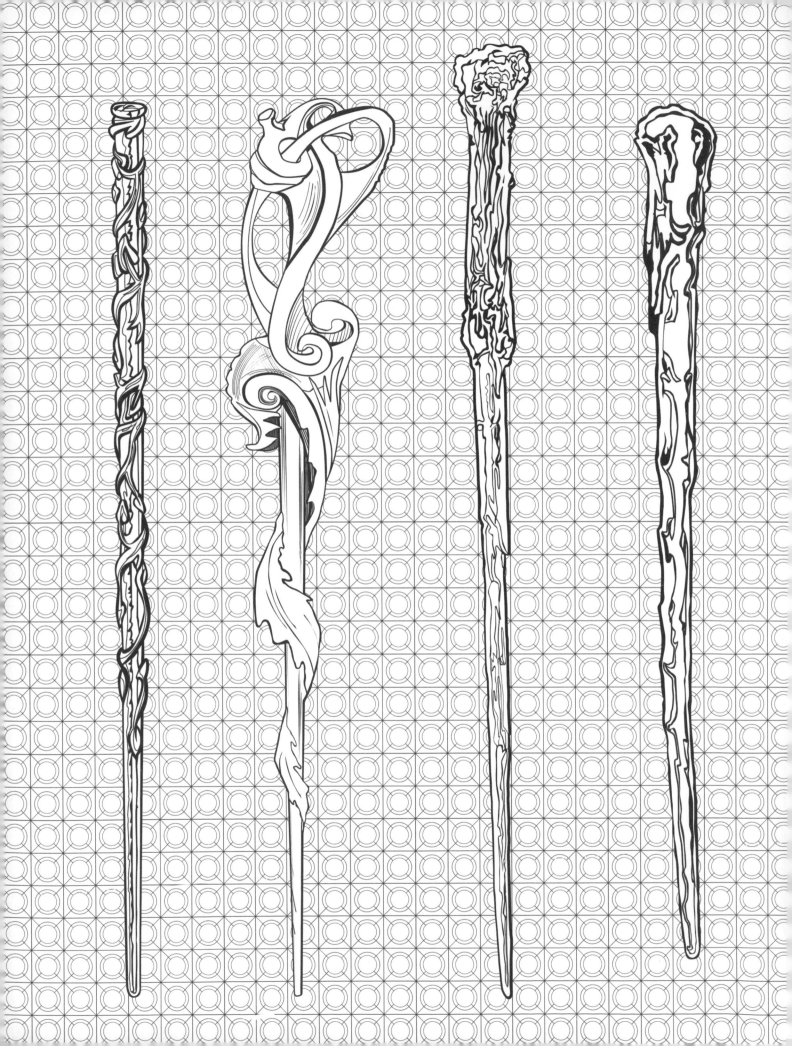

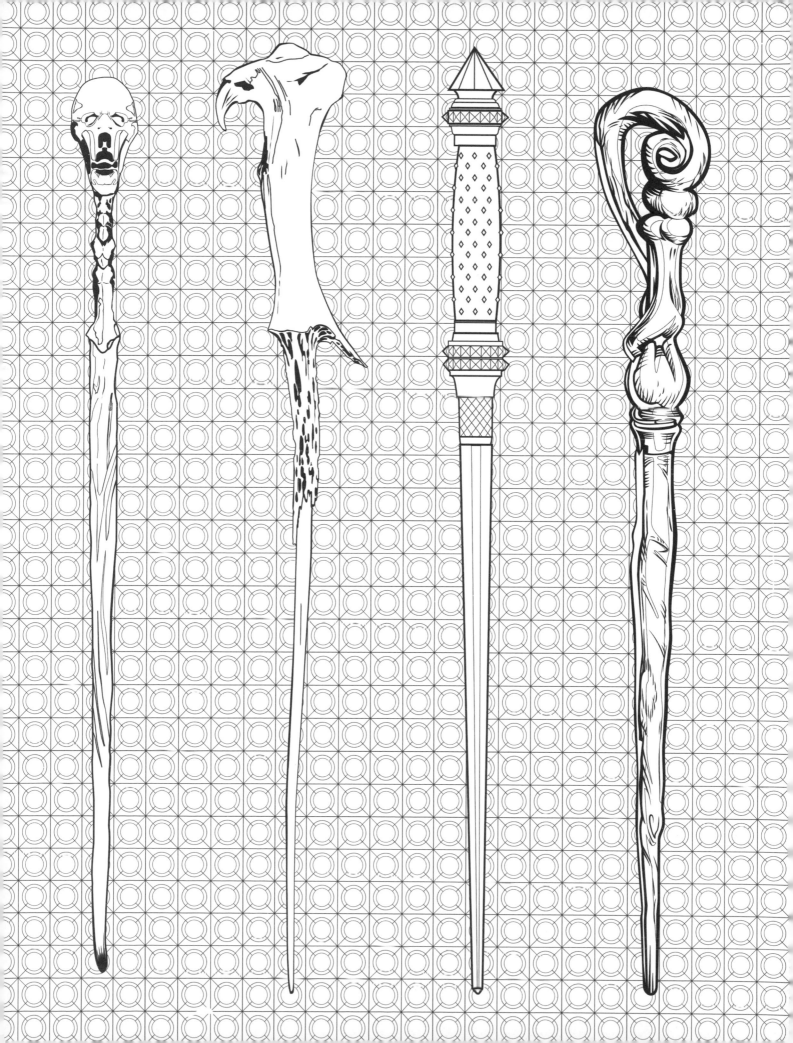

TOM MARVOLO RIDDLE

Harry Potter

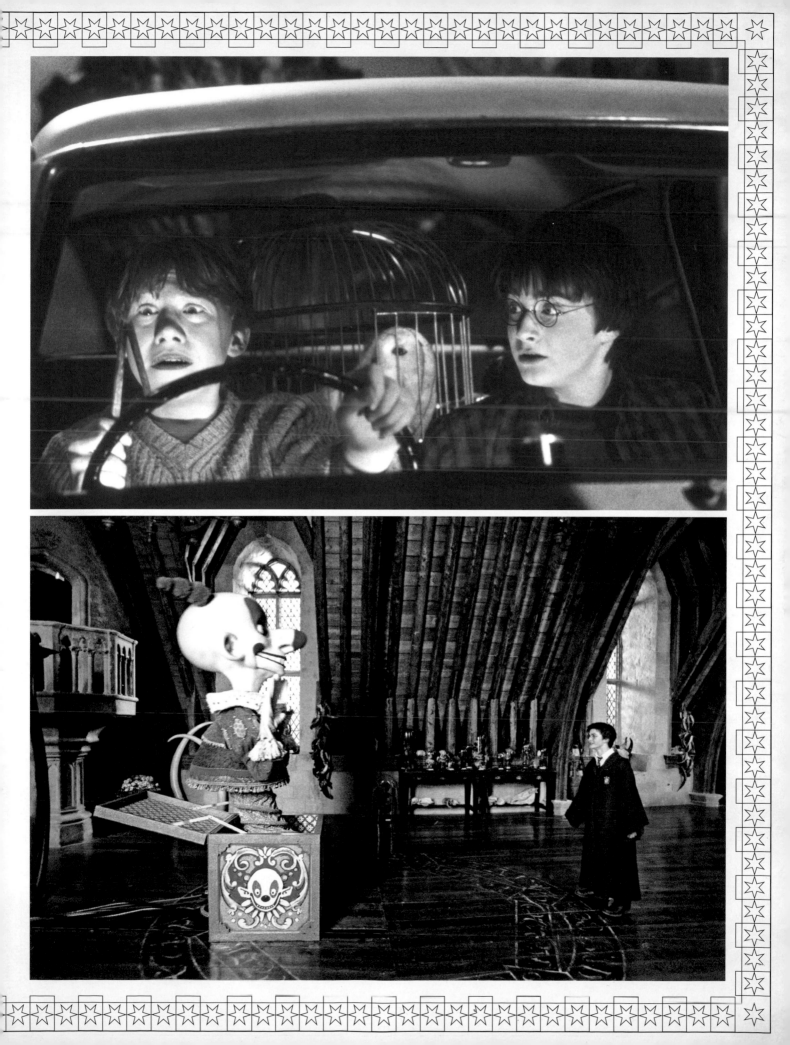

Published under license by Studio Press, an imprint of Templar Publishing,
part of the Bonnier Publishing Group.

The publisher does not have any control over and does not assume any
responsibility for author or third-party websites or their content.

No part of this publication may be reproduced, stored in a retrieval system, or
transmitted in any form or by any means, electronic, mechanical, photocopying,
recording, or otherwise, without written permission of the publisher. For
information regarding permission, write to Studio Press, The Plaza, 535 King's
Road, London, SW10 0SZ.

ISBN 978-1-78370-548-1

Art Credits:
Winged keys adapted from concept art by Gert Stevens
Quidditch World Cup Poster, Weasley Wizard Wheezes graphics, Owl Post sign,
Quibbler cover, and cauldron graphics by MinaLima Design
Grindylow and Dobby concept art by Rob Bliss
Quidditch, merperson, and troll tapestry concept art by Adam Brockbank
Wands by Rob Bliss, Ben Dennett, and Adam Brockbank
Concept art of Hogwarts Castle with deer by Dermot Power

Produced by

INSIGHT
EDITIONS
PO Box 3088
San Rafael, CA 94912
www.insighteditions.com

PUBLISHER: Raoul Goff
ART DIRECTOR: Chrissy Kwasnik
DESIGNER: Jenelle Wagner
EXECUTIVE EDITOR: Vanessa Lopez
PROJECT EDITOR: Greg Solano
PRODUCTION EDITOR: Rachel Anderson
PRODUCTION MANAGER: Blake Mitchum

Insight Editions would like to thank Victoria Selover, Elaine Piechowski, Melanie
Swartz, Adam Raiti, Rosemary Pinkham, Jon Glick, Alix Nicholaeff, and Erik Deangelis.

ROOTS of PEACE   REPLANTED PAPER

Insight Editions, in association with Roots of Peace, will plant two trees for each tree
used in the manufacturing of this book. Roots of Peace is an internationally renowned
humanitarian organization dedicated to eradicating land mines worldwide and converting
war-torn lands into productive farms and wildlife habitats. Roots of Peace will plant two
million fruit and nut trees in Afghanistan and provide farmers there with the skills and
support necessary for sustainable land use.

Manufactured in Italy by Insight Editions

10 9 8 7 6 5 4 3 2 1